CW00665903

"Let there be light" – *Genesis 1:3*

THE NON-ELECTRIC LIGHTING SERIES

BOOK 4: Kerosene Lamps

Ron Brown

R&C Publishing

Newark Valley, New York

Notice: This manual is designed to provide information on wick-type kerosene lamps and lanterns.

It is not the purpose of this guide to reprint all the information that is otherwise available, but to complement, amplify, and supplement other texts and resources. You are urged to read all the available material and learn as much as you can about flashlights and to tailor the information to your specific circumstances.

Every effort has been made to make this guide as complete and accurate as possible. However, there may be mistakes, both typographical and in content. Therefore this text should be used only as a general guide and not as the ultimate source of kerosene lamp information. Furthermore, this guide contains information that is current only up to the printing date.

The purpose of this manual is to educate and entertain. The views, opinions, positions, and strategies expressed by the author are his alone. The author makes no representations as to the accuracy, completeness, correctness, suitability, or validity of any information in this book and will not be liable for any errors, omissions, or delays in this information or any losses, injuries, or damages arising from its use.

ISBN 978-0-9905564-4-2

Published by
R&C Publishing
15 Dr. Knapp Road South
Newark Valley, NY 13811
Printed in the United States of America

THE NON-ELECTRIC LIGHTING SERIES

BOOK 4: **Kerosene Lamps**

TABLE OF CONTENTS

FOREWORD

Having been brought up in the age of electricity, the idea of providing light by any means other than a wall switch was foreign to me as a child. When the power went out, as it frequently did in those days, we resorted to candlelight and little else. It was not much fun.

Years later, while camping with friends, I was introduced to the world of kerosene lighting. Imagine that: a pitch black night with plenty of light to see faces, recognize the food on your plate, and read one of those scary novels that teens like to read while roughing it out in the wilderness.

As I look back in time, I remember observing, even as a child, that as long as there was bright light in the house, we could go about our business of living – eating, reading, playing games, and doing those things that families do as a matter of course. When the lights were out and all we had to see with was a flashlight with weak batteries or a stub of a candle, everything stopped. In most cases we crawled into bed and stayed there until the power came back on.

Now that I am an adult, I find myself much more knowledgeable about the ways of old when it comes to providing adequate light when the electricity is off. Even more, as someone who is avid about preparedness, I want to ensure that I can light up a room if the grid is down for a day, a week, a month or even longer. To that end, kerosene lighting is right up there on my list of preps along with extra flashlights, a stockpile of spare batteries, and propane lanterns.

In this, Ron Brown's latest book, you will learn everything you need to know about kerosene lamps:

what they are, how to use them safely, building your own, and what to look for when purchasing a vintage (meaning old and on-eBay) lamp. In this super-modern era when one is none and two is one, having some old-time knowledge about kerosene lamps might just be the answer to bright nights when the blackout lingers.

Kerosene lighting has a fascinating history and was an important part of our grandparents and great-grandparents daily life. Take a step back in time and learn about using kerosene lamps for emergency lighting. This book will only take a couple of hours to read and it will be time well spent. See if you don't agree.

Gaye Levy
March 2015

*****

Want to learn more about basic preparedness? Please visit Gaye's website at www.backdoorsurvival.com where you will find tools for creating a self-reliant lifestyle through thoughtful prepping and optimism.

*****

KEROSENE LAMP THEORY

My wife is from the Philippines and wick-type kerosene lamps such as the one pictured above were common in her youth. They were called 'dirty lamps.' Clean lamps (with chimneys) didn't smoke. She and her sister would take a dirty lamp under the mosquito netting to do their homework. In the morning they would have black smudges around their nostrils.

Frightful appearances notwithstanding, there are only a handful of principles that must be observed in order to have a *safe* wick-type lamp:

(1) It must burn a *combustible* fuel (e.g. kerosene), not a *flammable* fuel (e.g. gasoline).

(2) There can be no crack in the wick tube.

(3) The wick must fit snugly within the wick tube.

(4) The flame must be 1¾-inches minimum above the top of the fuel in the tank.

Just for the heck of it, let's build a homemade lamp and intentionally violate some of these rules. I think you'll find it interesting.

What happens if we use a flammable fuel?

It occurred to me that, in principle, a Zippo cigarette lighter is a miniature lamp. It has a font or tank that holds fuel. It has a wick that draws fuel to the flame by capillary action. Why couldn't a Zippo be used as a mini-lamp? Why not indeed?

Of course, Zippo fuel is 'flammable' white gas. So a Zippo-lamp makes a good example of what can happen in a wick-lamp burning a flammable fuel.

At this point, we need to understand two terms: 'flammable' and 'combustible.' Gasoline is a 'flammable' fuel. Below 100° F it will turn to a gas (evaporate), combine with oxygen, take fire, and burn in the open air.

Kerosene will not. Below 100° F kerosene will not evaporate fast enough to form a concentration sufficient to take flame. If you throw a lit match in a bucket of kerosene it will simply go out – *psst* – just as if it had been tossed into a bucket of water. Try that with gasoline and you will get a sheet of flame over the entire surface of the liquid.

Gasoline is termed 'flammable' whereas kerosene is 'combustible.'

2

All wick-fed lamps tend to 'run high.' That is, the lamp gets warm from the flame and the fuel gets warm from the lamp . . . and the warm fuel is thinner, more volatile . . . and the flame goes higher . . . than you desire . . .

So what will happen if we place a lit Zippo on the table and leave it there like a candle? Essentially, it will be a tiny kerosene lamp running on white gas. And let's surround it with a glass chimney. Then it will be less likely to get blown out by the wind.

■ **ABOVE:** *The set-up. The sliver of wood under the chimney allows air to enter the 'chamber' and reach the flame.* ■

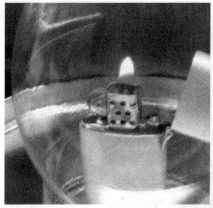

■ **ABOVE LEFT:** *Operating smoothly. Another of my wonderful ideas, thank you very much.* **ABOVE RIGHT:** *At the five-minute mark, the metal lighter is too hot to touch. Fumes, at or near autoignition temperature, seep out through every crack. When they reach some oxygen – Poof! – a runaway lamp. The flame shown here is coming from the entire perimeter of the lighter. Wick? We don't need no stinking wick.* ■

Cracked wick tube

A cracked wick tube (above left) will result in flame following the crack (above right). This is a dangerous situation. Shortly, the lamp will begin a distinctive hissing sound. Kerosene is vaporizing below the heat shield and in the tank. Lastly, think on this: glass shrapnel is darned difficult for the doctor to see when he attempts to pick it out of your body.

This wick tube has (what was intended to be) a butt joint. But it's a Dollar Store lamp, cheaply made, and you can see the crack where the metal does not quite come together. A crack, even a .002" crack (which is thinner than a piece of typing paper) will result in a runaway lamp. Not can or might, *will*.

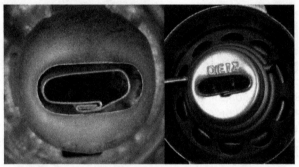

■ **ABOVE LEFT:** *Grooved joint from a 1940 'daisy lamp.'* **ABOVE RIGHT:** *Lap joint.* ■

Butt joints risk having a crack; *lap* joints suffice to eliminate the crack; but a *grooved* joint (to use proper sheet-metalworker terminology) is better yet. Cheap lamps use lap joints so I was disappointed to find a lap joint in my new Dietz lantern (made in China) – especially after I found that my neighbor's rusty old Dietz, made long ago in Syracuse, New York, had a grooved joint.

In one picture of an antique whale oil lamp I noticed a small cutout in the wick tube. What could that be? Then it dawned on me. It was a place to insert a pick and nudge the wick up or down to adjust the size of the flame – without disturbing the flame. Clever. But, although it might have been okay on whale oil with a flash point of 570° F, would

5

it work with kerosene? I copied the antique design as best I could . . .

■ **ABOVE:** *I don't know about you, but this is not my idea of 'working' with kerosene. This was after just two minutes. It reinforces the point once again that we cannot have a crack or gap or break in the wick tube. Still, what if we installed a metal heat shield between the flame and the gap?* ■

■ **ABOVE:** *Aha! The copper heat shield did an amazing job of dissipating heat. I even laid a strike anywhere match head*

on the shield and left it there for half an hour. It did not ignite even though I intentionally let the kerosene flame run high. ■

■ **ABOVE:** *The heat shield puts us very close to the design of a modern kerosene lamp. Instead of a pointed nail or some such to reach in the gap and adjust the wick height, we could use a spur gear (pictured above). That, plus a chimney, and we'd have a contemporary kerosene lamp.* ■

The wick must fit snugly

This is a book on emergency lighting. And I wondered if you could substitute, in an emergency, a narrow wick in a lamp that called for a wide one. **No!**

It seems harmless enough. But remember how the flame followed the crack in a wick tube? Well, the flame will follow an opening – such as is shown here – right down into the font (fuel tank).

When I tried the narrow-for-wide wick substitution, I was using a clear glass font. I lit the narrow wick and all seemed well. I busied myself with other tasks in the shop when suddenly the flame was sucked right down inside the font. It swirled around in there – I could see it through the glass – and I honest-to-God thought it was going to blow up.

It didn't. Fortunately the font was over half full of fuel (which means the oxygen supply was small) and the flame died out in just a few seconds. I've had two or three scary moments with lamps and lanterns but that was the worst.

The flame must be 1¾ inches above the fuel

I measured a whole bunch of kerosene lamps – antiques, brand new ones, boudoir lamps with round wicks, flat-wick lamps, lanterns, Duplexes, Rayos, Aladdins – and every one was designed such that the flame was a minimum of 1¾" away from the oil in the tank. Most, in fact, were more than that – a Rayo was 2¾".

Why? Why do we need that distance? Well, we don't – with vegetable oil as the fuel and a flash point over 400° F. But a conventional wick-fed lamp on kerosene is a different animal.

There was an experiment in Book 3, *Lamp Fuels*, where we brought a lit match close to a teaspoon of gasoline. The gasoline ignited before the flame ever touched the spoon. The point is that, with a wick lamp, the further apart we keep the flame from the fuel, the safer we are.

Kerosene didn't ignite in that experiment even when the flame touched the edge of the spoon (*at room temperature*). But if we preheat the kerosene, at some point it *will* ignite.

Go back and look at the picture of the Indonesian woman at the beginning of this book. Note the fuel level in her lamp. It's hot at the equator where she lives. The fuel in her lamp is warm before she ever touches a match to its wick. I doubt she ever fills that lamp beyond halfway. The distance between the flame and the fuel (1) keeps any fuel vapor in the tank at a distance from an ignition source and (2) keeps the kerosene cool, slowing its evaporation rate.

I suspect the 1¾" figure for *kerosene* was derived by trial and error a hundred years ago. But, be it the crude hand-made lamp I bought in Malaysia from a street vendor or a costly European antique, 1¾" appears to be the magic minimum. It may appear arbitrary, but I, personally, don't plan to violate it just to see what happens.

Candlepower

In this book, when you find a statement like, "Lamp XYZ is equivalent to a 40-watt light bulb," you might well ask how I came to such a conclusion. Fair question.

This section on lamp design is perhaps as good a place as any to introduce candlepower. It's a topic that gets very complicated very quickly. So let's keep it simple.

Foot-candles. If you light a candle, the amount of light that it generates one foot away from itself is called a *foot-candle*.

9

Lumens. A *lumen* is a unit of measurement equal to one foot-candle falling on one square foot of area.

Candlepower. One *candlepower* equals 12.57 lumens. Google for it if you want to know where the 12.57 comes from. But I'll put up even money that, if you do Google for it, after two minutes you won't *care*.

Candlepower was defined in 1860, redefined in 1909, defined again in 1921, and redefined again in 1937. In 1948 the term candlepower was declared obsolete and was replaced by the term candela.

Candela? "The candela is the luminous intensity, in a given direction, of a source that emits monochromatic radiation of frequency 540×10^{12} hertz and that has a radiant intensity in that direction of $1/683$ watt per steradian." – *General Conference on Weights and Measures*

Steradian? "A steradian is defined as the solid angle subtended at the center of a sphere of radius r by a portion of the surface of the sphere whose area, A, equals r^2." – *McGraw-Hill Dictionary of Scientific and Technical Terms*

Too technical? It could be worse. We've neglected the French unit *carcels* altogether.

Okay. We have not answered the 12.57 question but does anybody still care?

An electric light bulb – an ordinary incandescent bulb – produces 15 lumens of light output for every watt of electrical input. A 100-watt light bulb thus produces 1500 lumens or 119 candlepower ($1500 \div 12.57 = 119$).

Sometimes I have trouble remembering which is bigger, candlepower or wattage. If the Aladdin box says *60 watts*, is the candlepower equivalency bigger or smaller than 60? Here's a limerick to help:

There once was a candle named Power
Who had a half-brother named Watt.
Though Power was bigger
They had equal vigor.
The girls found them equally hot.

This all works fine, it seems to me, down in the range of 40 and 100-watt light bulbs. But as the candlepower number gets bigger the system becomes progressively distorted.

A Coleman Model 237 lantern, for example, is rated (some would say overrated) at 500 candlepower, theoretically equivalent to a 420-watt light bulb. It is not.

Given an old-time Coleman Silk-Lite No. 1111 mantle, a Coleman 237 puts out light equivalent to a 275-watt light bulb. Make the comparison yourself and see if you don't agree. Although 275 is extremely bright, 275 does not equal 420.

This is not a jab at Coleman. My thesis is this: the bigger the numbers, the more the distortion. There's *some* distortion down in the 500 candlepower range. But I have a flashlight that is billed as producing 15 *million* candlepower. Merciful heavens! That should be equivalent to having every room in my house filled floor-to-ceiling with 100-watt bulbs. You should be able to see this thing from outer space.

My rating system gives different results from what the manufacturers claim. First I light the lamp to be tested. Then I put an electric bulb beside it. I own the following wattages: 4, 5, 7, 7½, 15, 25, 30, 40, 50, 60, 70, 75, 100, 135, 150, 200, 240, 250, 300.

Then I visually compare the lamp being tested with the electric bulb. Remember, this is something you can do yourself.

When in doubt, I call in the neighbor's kid for a second opinion. The other option would be to go back and figure out where the 12.57 came from. Even then, would we believe the numbers? Or our own eyes? That is the question.

■ ABOVE: *The neighbor's kid.* ■

KEROSENE LAMP PRACTICE

The previous section was entitled "Kerosene Lamp *Theory*." This section is "Kerosene Lamp *Practice*." Please remember that, in theory, theory and practice are the same. But in practice they're not.

Here we'll cover (1) parts of a flat-wick lamp, (2) safe operation, (3) wick trimming, and (4) styles of wick-fed lamps and lanterns.

Parts of a Lamp

The Wick

The wick brings fuel to the flame by capillary action. After you install a new wick and fill the lamp with fuel for use, let it set for half an hour before lighting; allow the wick to become saturated.

Dirty fuel or dyed fuel or thick fuel (e.g. diesel) will gradually plug a wick. A bath in white gas (Coleman fuel) does a fair job of cleaning a dirty wick.

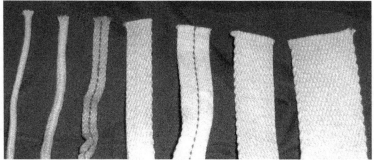

■ ABOVE: ⅛" round; ³/₁₆" round; ⅜" flat; ⅝" flat; ¹³/₁₆" flat; 1" flat; 1½" flat. This is not a comprehensive list by any means. It's just what I happened to have at hand when I decided I needed a picture. ■

Wicks don't last forever. About ⅛" of wick is consumed for every gallon of fuel burned.

If you're having trouble threading a new wick through its wick tube, moisten it with a bit of fuel to provide lubrication. Just about any cotton cloth you can coax through the wick tube will serve as a wick. A triple thickness of old denim blue-jean material works surprisingly well.

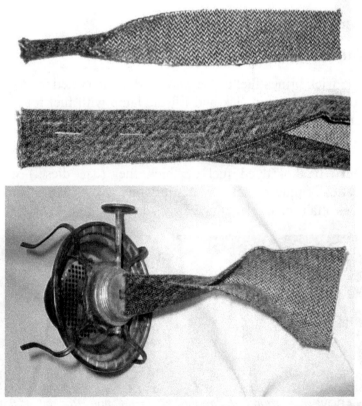

■ **TOP:** *For round-wick miniature lamps.* **CENTER:** *For flat-wick lamps. (Stapling is easier than sewing.)* **BOTTOM:** *What's not to like?* ■

Fiberglass Wicks

Round (like rope) fiberglass wicks work okay in miniature boudoir lamps that have a spur-gear feed mechanism for the wick.

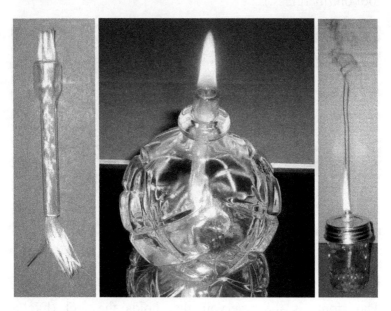

That being said, in the lamps pictured here, the wick (inside a 2" long glass tube) is advanced manually with tweezers and picks. The teeniest, tiniest bit of over-adjustment and the lamp is indistinguishable from the smoky/primitive Indonesian lamp shown at the beginning of this book.

Round fiberglass wicks range in diameter from $^1/_{16}$" to $^3/_4$" (which is pretty huge). The big sizes are used for patio tiki torches. They will last longer than cotton.

I was pleased to locate some flat fiberglass wicking. Unfortunately, it was too thin and too slippery to be of practical use in a flat-wick lamp or lantern. The spurs of the feed mechanism of my Dietz lantern would simply not grab the slippery fiberglass and   advance the wick.

In short, I'm not a big fan. Cotton wicking is easier to locate (for purchase), easier to feed through the wick tube, and easier to trim. (Though, for whatever help it may be, a square-across toenail clipper makes a pretty fair trimming tool on fiberglass.)

Fonts and Collars

The 'font' is the reservoir that holds the fuel (like a baptismal font holds water). The metal collar on top of the font may be screwed on or cemented in place. The collar fastens the burner to the font.

The Burner

We already know a lot about the burner: (1) it is threaded on its base to mate with the collar, (2) it has a wick tube that holds the wick, (3) a spur gear is used to drive the wick up and down (a wick-wheel or wick-winder propels the gear), and (4) it has a heat shield between the flame and the slot in the wick tube where the spur gear engages the wick. If you peer down an empty wick tube, you can see the teeth of the spur gear.

There are a couple of other things the burner does. It has vertical tines to hold the chimney in place. And it has a floor plate under the chimney with holes punched in it so that air can feed the flame. (Remember, back in the beginning of this book, I had to put a sliver of wood as a spacer under the chimney on the makeshift Zippo lamp?) And it has a shroud, like an upside-down funnel, that directs the air to the flame.

■ **ABOVE LEFT:** *A shroud.* **ABOVE RIGHT:** *A burner with the shroud in place.* ■

Can you run a kerosene lamp without the shroud? <u>Answer</u>. Yes. But you can run the flame higher and get more light if the shroud is installed.

The Chimney

The base of the chimney that fits into the burner is called the *fitter*. That's the term in common use amongst lamp aficionados but is not a definition in any dictionary. The actual, measured, fitter diameter of 'ordinary' chimneys is 2⅞" (with a chimney height of 8½"). Miniature chimneys have a typical fitter diameter of 1¼".

It was discovered long ago that a bulge in the chimney above the flame directed the airflow such that a larger flame could be run than would otherwise be possible.

Nominal Dimensions

You will hear terms like Nutmeg burner, Queen Anne No. 2 burner, etc. What do they mean? Looks like we need a table of sizes and dimensions. Unfortunately, the table value won't necessarily match what your ruler tells you. We need to understand the draftsman's concept of *nominal*.

Burner Style	Fits Collar Opening	Approx. Chimney Fitter Size	Wick Size (Width)	Lamp Type
Small Pixie	$^{13}/_{16}$"	$1^{3}/_{16}$" OD	$^{1}/_{8}$" round	Miniature
No. 00 Nutmeg & Acorn	$^{5}/_{8}$"	$1^{1}/_{8}$"	$^{3}/_{8}$" flat	True Miniature
Dietz Burner	$^{7}/_{8}$"	$1^{1}/_{4}$"	$^{3}/_{4}$"	Small Lamp
No. 0 Hornet	$^{7}/_{8}$"	$1^{1}/_{2}$" to $1^{5}/_{8}$"	$^{1}/_{2}$"	True Miniature
No. 0 Eagle Burners	$^{7}/_{8}$"	$2^{1}/_{16}$" to $2^{1}/_{8}$"	$^{1}/_{2}$"	Small Finger L.
No. 1 Gem Artic	$^{7}/_{8}$"	$1^{1}/_{2}$" to $1^{5}/_{8}$"	$^{1}/_{2}$"	True Miniature
No. 1 Burners	$^{7}/_{8}$"	$2^{1}/_{2}$"	$^{5}/_{8}$"	Small Lamp
No. 2 Brass Plated Burners	$1^{3}/_{16}$"	3"	$^{13}/_{16}$"	
No. 2 Burners (Queen & Eagle)	$1^{3}/_{16}$"	3"	1"	
No. 3 Burners	$1^{3}/_{4}$"	3"	$1^{1}/_{2}$"	
Vapor Burner	N/A	N/A	$^{7}/_{8}$"	
Pixie & Japanese Burners	$^{7}/_{8}$"	$1^{1}/_{4}$"	N/A	
No. 6 Kosmos Burners	$^{31}/_{32}$"	$1^{15}/_{16}$"	$1^{3}/_{8}$"	
No. 8 Kosmos Burners	$1^{1}/_{16}$"	$1^{7}/_{16}$"	$1^{5}/_{8}$"	
No 10 Kosmos Burners	$1^{1}/_{4}$"	$1^{9}/_{16}$"	$1^{15}/_{16}$"	
Various European Burners	N/A	$1^{7}/_{8}$"	N/A	
No. 14 Kosmos	$1^{1}/_{2}$"	2" to $2^{1}/_{16}$"	$2^{9}/_{16}$"	
No. 15 Matador	$1^{1}/_{2}$"	2" to $2^{1}/_{16}$"	N/A	
English Duplex & Success	$1^{1}/_{2}$"	$2^{1}/_{2}$"	$1^{1}/_{16}$"	
Rayo Burners	$2^{1}/_{4}$"	$2^{5}/_{8}$"	$2^{1}/_{2}$"	
Central Draft Burners	$2^{3}/_{8}$"	$2^{5}/_{8}$"	$2^{1}/_{2}$"	
Aladdin Burners	$2^{1}/_{8}$"	$2^{5}/_{8}$"	$1^{1}/_{8}$"	

The 3" fitter size in the chart above is a 'nominal' figure, corresponding to my $2^{7}/_{8}$" actual measured diameter for an 'ordinary' chimney. So what's going on? This chart is from www.bplampsupply.com/help/05HowToKeroBurner.php.

Let's see if I can clarify. If you walk into a hardware store and ask the clerk for a ½" black iron pipe nipple, he'll walk back to the appropriate bin and say over his shoulder, "How long did you want?" The ½" refers to the pipe's diameter.

19

BUT nothing about the pipe measures ½" – *nothing!* Not the inside diameter (ID), not the outside diameter (OD). Not the root diameter nor the crest diameter.

One-half inch is for talking purposes only. The clerk knows ½" pipe when he sees it. It's a trade term. Usage is king. In the shop, just as in any language, usage rules.

The dimensions used in this inquiry are actual, measured dimensions determined by rulers and calipers and feeler gauges. The dimensions found in various charts are nominal dimensions (sometimes). They may bear little resemblance to reality.

The International Guild of Lamp Researchers has an excellent Web site devoted to non-electric lighting and maintains extensive archives. Guild question #200 deals with 'lines.' What does the term *line* or *ligne* mean? It's apparently a measure of diameter (or a trait that can be converted to diameter) used in watchmaking, lampmaking, and antique firearms. Some say it's the inside diameter of a tubular wick pressed flat and varies with the wick's thickness. It's an old fashioned term. Today, *line* cannot be reconciled to any actual measurement or measurement system – metric, Imperial Measure, French, Swedish, German, old or new.

After pages of wheel-spinning, one contributor (John from England) said, "Everybody knows what . . . a fifteen line lamp is . . . why complicate matters."

Exactly. I suspect that 'line' is and was a nominal measurement, like ½" pipe. It doesn't match the actual measurement of any physical characteristic and never did.

The Fuel

Fuel is part of the system that produces light. A typical flat-wick lamp with a ⅛"-wide wick generates light equivalent to a 7½-watt nightlight. In a simple flat-wick lamp, kerosene, mineral spirits, and diesel fuel deliver equivalent amounts of light.

So your choice boils down to cost, availability, and smell. Smell-wise, kerosene may be the worst of the bunch although it was once the best. K-1 kerosene contains 400 ppm sulfur. And it's the sulfur that does most of the smelling. (Parts per million or ppm is explained in Book 3 of The Non-Electric Lighting Series, *Lamp Fuels*).

Diesel fuel (for highway use) is 15 ppm. Odorless mineral spirits is under 5 ppm. Admittedly, sulfur is not the only aromatic ingredient but it is by far the biggest offender.

Trimming the Wick

Trimming a new wick with a razor blade or scissors leaves whiskers of fabric that produce strange spikes of flame. Better to dip the end of the wick in kerosene, burn off that kerosene (with the wick mounted in the lamp), then trim the charred wick-end with your fingers. Touch it up – and wash the chimney – every day.

Most people trim straight across, using the wick tube as a guide. Some prefer a dome effect, higher in the center. My dad always insisted that a double-dome (a valley in the center with a dome on each end) produced the most light. And he may have been right. A double-dome would give you the most lineal inches of flame. It's not something the novice will master in his first year, however.

21

Lamp Operation

1. Fill the lamp with fuel.
2. Wait for the wick to become saturated.
3. Remove the chimney.
4. Raise the wick slightly above the wick tube.
5. Light the wick; a wooden match works best.
6. Replace the chimney.
7. Let the lamp thoroughly preheat on low before turning it up (too high an initial flame can crack the glass chimney).
8. While running, if smoke comes out the top of the chimney, the lamp is turned too high.

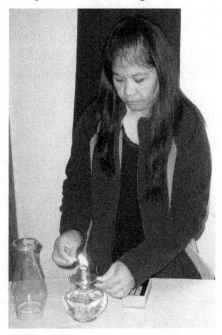

TO EXTINGUISH
1. Lower the flame, then blow across the top of the chimney into your cupped palm. (At least that's what the books say. You may end up blowing down the chimney tube anyway).

2. As soon as the flame goes out, lower the wick into the wick tube to minimize smoldering and smell.

Lamp & Lantern Styles

■ **ABOVE:** *'Miniature' lamps use round, rope-like wicks and give off as much light as a candle.* ■

■ **ABOVE:** *A simple flat-wick lamp cranked to the max.* ■

■ **ABOVE:** *A flat-wick lamp with a built-in loop is called a 'finger lamp.' The loop is more cosmetic than practical; it does not really make for a safe one-handed carry.* ■

■ **ABOVE LEFT:** *A new $6 lamp from Dollar General. It has a ⅛"-wide wick. Repeat after me: A more expensive lamp will not give more light. Only a wider wick will do that.* **ABOVE RIGHT:** *A Dietz barn lantern. Compare the size of the base on the lantern to the base of the house-lamp on the left. Which one would be the most stable when setting outside on the ground?* ■

Lanterns (as opposed to lamps) are made for outside use. They're constructed of metal so they won't break if bumped or dropped. The chimney of a lantern is called a 'globe.' It's shorter and rounder (and thicker) than a lamp chimney and is held securely in place within a wire basket.

Wick-type lanterns come in three flavors – hot blast, cold blast, and dead flame.

Dead flame lanterns are basically enclosures to protect the flame. Fresh air enters through vents and is exhausted up the chimney. UCO and Coleman candle-lanterns are dead flame (see Book 1 of The Non-Electric Lighting Series: *Candles*).

All hot blast and cold blast lanterns are *tubular* lanterns (note the metal tubes that run up the sides of the lantern in the above picture). Hot blast lanterns are designed to recirculate some of the combustion air. They are recommended for inside use because a percentage of the exhaust fumes are recirculated and consumed in the flame.

Cold blast lanterns use fresh air to feed the flame. According to the catalogues, cold blast lanterns have a brighter and whiter light than hot blast.

As a practical matter we're talking about small increments of light down in the 7½-watt nightlight range. If you are ever called upon to set up a tent in the dark exclusively by the light of a wick-type kerosene lantern – no flashlights allowed – you ain't gonna enjoy it very much.

A bit of trivia. The word lantern is a corruption of the word lanthorne. The 'horn' part of lant*horn*e is the key. Thinly shaved pieces of cow's horn were once used for the lantern's windows. The horn was more durable than oiled paper. It was later replaced by mica (isinglass) and later yet by borosilicate glass (Pyrex).

DUPLEX

After the basic flat-wick lamp, the next logical step up in complexity is the Duplex. In essence it's the same as a flat-wick – except there are *two* wicks.

In 1839, Joseph Hinks of Birmingham, England, took over his brother's lighting works, James Hinks & Co. Twenty-six years later, he – Joseph – patented the Duplex lamp. It appears that Duplexes were made by both E.M. Duplex Co. as well as Hinks though the history of neither enterprise is readily available (at least to a Yank like me). The Encyclopædia Britannica does not have an entry for either 'Hinks' or 'Duplex.'

Due to blackouts and power interruptions, Duplexes (notwithstanding their quasi-antique status) were used extensively in England during World War II. They produced light on par with a 35-watt light bulb. Based on what I've been able to glean from eBay advertisements, Duplexes may have been manufactured right up into the 1980's. The advertising slogan was, "Two wicks are better than one but three are not better than two." Catchy, huh?

Until recently, Duplexes in the USA were only available as antiques (and British antiques at that). The only practical way to obtain a Duplex was to build one from parts. Doing so, however, soon led to the discovery that there were several models and the parts were not interchangeable. The Duplex burner you just bought on eBay didn't screw into the Duplex font you'd been saving. (Well, the seller *claimed* it was a Duplex font.)

Today, Hong Kong knockoffs are available through Lehman's (an on-line and catalog store catering to non-electric living). With the advent of the knockoffs, the 'duplex' has come to be regarded as a *design* – a lamp having two wicks – rather than a brand.

The Duplex chimney

Two things are critical to the performance of a Duplex – the chimney and the wicks.

The Duplex chimney is oval. The fitter (i.e. the bottom end of the chimney that fits into the burner) is round. And the top of the chimney, where exhaust fumes exit the lamp, is also round. In the center, however, the chimney is oval – as if the glass blower formed a perfectly round chimney tube, then laid it on the floor and stepped on it.

The Duplex fitter is 2½" in diameter. Therefore a Rayo chimney (2⅝") won't fit nor will a 'regular' chimney (2⅞"). I do have a round chimney (matador style, described elsewhere) with a 2½" fitter, and a Duplex runs on it, but light output drops from 35 to 25 watts.

In use, the flattened bulge in the chimney must be parallel to the wicks.

Duplex wicks

Hattersley Narrow Fabrics of Yorkshire, England makes authentic Duplex wicks. I was lucky enough to locate a collector in Canada who sold me a few. They have two purple stripes and are $1^1/_{16}''$ wide. Anything else gives less light. Today, there are a couple of places on-line that sell Duplex/Hattersley wicks (see 'Availability' below).

Burning a Wick

In any wick-fed lamp, the wick and the fuel collaborate to produce a flame. Each wick has a fuel that works best and vice versa. A wick that is not up to the job of lifting a thick, syrupy fuel results in a small flame.

The lamp operator, to get more light, turns up the wick. And, temporarily, more light is produced. It comes from the additional fuel on the newly exposed wick.

But that fuel is soon consumed and the light dies back to where it was before. So the operator again turns up the wick. Repeating the process over and over, the operator burns wick as much as he burns fuel.

The fuel-wick-chimney balance on a Duplex is tricky. An oval chimney plus Hattersley wicks plus kerosene produces 35 watts-worth of light. Diesel fuel will only produce 25 watts-worth. If you push the lamp beyond its 'natural limits,' burned wicks result.

Feeder Wicks

Feeder wicks are one way to improve Duplex performance.

Some Duplex burners come equipped with a wire bracket, located between the wick tubes, that holds a third wick. The third wick does not burn. It hangs from the bracket down into the oil and feeds extra fuel to the two main wicks that sport the actual flames.

None of my Duplex burners had that bracket. So I mounted one (see below). It's just a bent piece of wire (I used a coathanger), soldered in place. And below that please see the 'feeder wick' installed.

In the case of kerosene, my feeder wick boosted light output from 35 watts to 40 watts. In the case of diesel fuel, however, the feeder wick did not improve light output at all. On diesel, light output was 25 watts both before and after.

Snuffer

The lever opposite the wick-winder knobs trips a 'snuffer' that extinguishes the flame(s). Snuffers work great but not all Duplex burners have them.

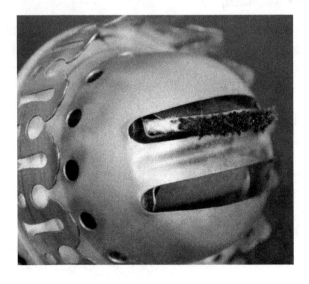

The Hong Kong duplex

For the balance of this section, the term 'English Duplex' will designate the original British brand name whereas 'Hong Kong duplex' (with a small 'd') will designate the foreign-made knock-off. Both have two wicks although differences do exist.

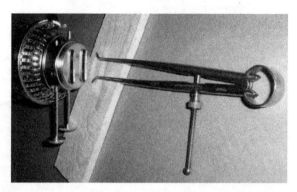

■ **ABOVE:** *The wick tubes of a Hong Kong duplex are slightly wider than an English Duplex.* ■

Duplex availability

To have a Duplex you need (1) a burner, (2) an oval chimney, (3) Hattersley wicks, and (4) a Duplex font (or an adaptor that will let you mount a Duplex burner on a regular font). No one vendor carries everything. The links below are valid today and will get you started but, like everything in life, they'll change over time; the links will change and what the vendors sell will change.

● Burner. I've found three places on-line to buy new English Duplex burners: [1] BP Lamp Supply in Tennessee; [2] South Lamp & Supply in North Carolina; and [3] Associated Kerosene & Oil Lamps Australia Braidwood. None of these suppliers carry the entire lamp

• <u>Chimney</u>. Two places carry oval chimneys: [1] <u>Lehman's</u> and [2] Associated Kerosene in Australia.

• <u>Wicks</u>. There are two on-line vendors that sell Hattersley wicks: [1] <u>Miles Stairs Wick Shop</u> and [2] <u>Old Flames Limited, UK</u>. Non-Hattersley wicks, $1^1/_{16}"$ wide, are sold by [1] Associated Kerosene in Australia and [2] Lehman's.

• <u>Entire Lamp</u>. The only place I know of to buy an entire lamp (new) is Lehman's. They call it 'The Daisy.' It is a knock-off Hong Kong duplex, not an English Duplex.

• <u>Adaptor</u>. Lehman's carries an adaptor (with which to mount a duplex burner on a regular font). Unfortunately, it is sold only in combination with a Hong Kong duplex burner, not separately. Associated Kerosene in Australia sells an adaptor as a stand-alone item.

Hong Kong duplex: the good

A whole lamp is available new. You don't have to build one from parts. And they're relatively inexpensive. A complete Daisy from Lehman's is $55 whereas a working English Duplex (complete with oval chimney, Hattersley wicks, etc.) on eBay runs over $300 – if you can find one.

■ **ABOVE:** *Lehman's Hong Kong duplex has a snuffer. Put a smiley face on that.* ■

I bought a burner-plus-adaptor from Lehman's. The good news was that the burner came equipped with two red-striped wicks that gave better performance than Hattersley wicks. That really surprised me. The red-striped wicks produced light at a 40-watt level instead of 35. (I assume the Daisy lamp – the entire lamp as sold by Lehman's – comes with the same red-striped wicks but that's only an assumption on my part.)

Hong Kong duplex: the bad

If you buy a burner-plus-adaptor (rather than the whole lamp), there are two things Lehman's neglects to tell you:

(1) You need an oval chimney with a 2½" fitter. That's a unique size. Lehman's sells the correct chimney but they don't tell you it's required. So if you order just the burner (expecting a chimney you already own to fit) you'll be disappointed.

(2) The adaptor is high-quality machined brass and will fit your $6 lamp from Dollar General but it will not screw on. The new collar-adaptor is slightly oversize, has no threads, and must be *cemented* in place. They don't tell you that. You get the part in the box with no instructions; as in zero.

What's the cement? <u>Answer</u>: Plaster of Paris.

■ **ABOVE:** *The old flat-wick burner is shown unscrewed from the collar and the old collar is shown unscrewed from the font. The replacement collar/adaptor (lower left) does not screw onto the font; it must be cemented in place.* ■

■ **ABOVE:** *The shroud on a Hong Kong duplex is removable from the burner. But it's a loose fit and shifts around like my trousers when I've been on a diet. It shouldn't do that.* ■

The Hong Kong duplex is inexpensive. And that's good. But you get what you pay for. It's flimsily made. The metal is thin. 'Fit and finish' (to use proper Quality Engineering terminology) is sloppy.

Hong Kong duplex: the ugly

The red-striped wick (far left) is the best, producing light at a 40-watt level. But there's nowhere to buy a replacement. *And it's too bulky to feed through an English Duplex burner* – making its superiority a very hollow claim to fame. Lehman's generic replacement wicks (far right) only produces light at a 25-watt level.

Duplex summary

You can buy brand new duplexes and that's a big plus. But the quality of Hong Kong duplexes is low and building an English Duplex from parts, though doable, is a pain in the neck. Fuel flexibility is good; a duplex will run on mineral spirits, kerosene, and diesel. Light output is good. But to get that light you must have Hattersley wicks and an oval chimney. All in all, a lot of horsing around. In the USA, there are simpler solutions.

RAYO

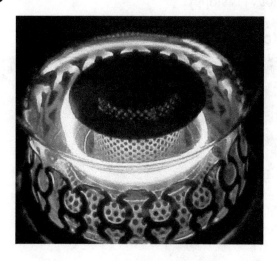

Centerdraft lamps have a tubular wick, like a sock, producing a circular flame. The best-known centerdraft is the Rayo. Made into the 1950's, Rayo's are still available on the second-hand market. There always seems to be a few complete Rayos on eBay.

Of course, used eBay lamps come without a users' manual. So a lot of this section deals with how to service a Rayo – change the wick and so on.

Back in the day, Rayo had a lot of competitors. And many were higher quality than the Rayo. B&H is a good example. But for today's users the competitors of old suffer from a variety of ills – bastard-size wicks and chimneys, lack of spare parts.

Another circular-flame lamp (available brand new) is the Kosmos. Unfortunately, the Kosmos only outputs light in the 25-watt range whereas a Rayo cruises comfortably at 40 watts. We'll discuss the Kosmos shortly.

Rayos were sold by Standard Oil. World War I was their heyday. But Standard Oil did not itself manufacture Rayos. They were made on contract for Standard Oil by a variety of lamp manufacturers.

Although Rayos produce a lot of light, thrifty kerosene consumption was never a strong suit. They were designed to maximize both light and fuel consumption. But what would you expect from a lamp distributed by a kerosene company for the purpose of promoting kerosene sales?

The Rayo wick surrounds a metal tube in the center of the lamp. This creates a chimney effect. Air flows up the center of the tube, resulting in greater combustion.

In engineering lingo, the Rayo is a robust design. It can be patched together in a multitude of ways and continue working. It can burn mineral spirits and diesel fuel in addition to kerosene. Admittedly, diesel fuel only generates light down in the 25-watt range but even that is far ahead of a candle.

And − once I realized that both paint thinner and charcoal lighter fluid were made from mineral spirits − and that fuel oil for home heating was virtually synonymous with diesel fuel − I began to comprehend that a whole array of alternate fuels existed.

Rayo availability

As mentioned earlier, Rayos were manufactured right up into the 1950's. Today, Rayos must be purchased second-hand, eBay being the prime source. A good 'user' lamp − meaning it has a few dings and is not a fancy display piece − will set you back $30 to $70.

Rayos are not particularly rare. Millions were originally made. They were plain-vanilla lamps for the common man. The 1908 Sears-Roebuck catalog had them for $2.

Because so many were made, spare parts are readily available. And the parts are interchangeable. There is only one size of chimney, one size of wick, one size of flame spreader. Any Rayo burner will screw into any Rayo font. Very few (if any) other brands feature this interchangeability of parts.

The necessities

A Rayo requires the following components to operate successfully: font, filler cap, gallery, wick-riser assembly, wick, flame spreader, and chimney. Complicated? Perhaps. But Grandma always found Rayos easier to understand than cell phones.

■ **ABOVE LEFT:** *Font with filler cap. The font holds the fuel. The cap prevents the fuel from spilling.* **CAUTION.** *See how the centerdraft tube sticks up above the font? On Rayos that have been electrified, you'll often find the tube has been sawed off. Unfortunately, I don't know how to undo that condition and convert the lamp back to kerosene.* **ABOVE RIGHT:** *Wick-riser assembly and wick. The riser assembly holds the wick.* ■

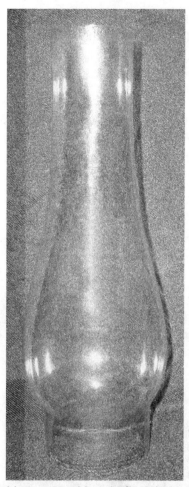

■ **ABOVE:** *The chimney provides draft and shapes the flame. A Rayo chimney has a fitter diameter of 2⅝" and a height of 9¾". (The typical chimney used on a flat-wick lamp has a fitter diameter of 2⅞" and is 8½" tall. It will not fit on a Rayo.)* ■

It is possible (I've seen it done) to pry back the ears or tines on a Rayo gallery and force it to accept a 'regular' chimney with a 2⅞" fitter. The holes or spaces that remain in the bottom of the gallery can be blocked with masking tape. An ugly arrangement to be sure, and of questionable safety, but it can get you through a rough patch.

■ **ABOVE LEFT:** *Gallery. The gallery holds the chimney.* **ABOVE RIGHT:** *Flame spreader. The flame spreader shapes the flame.* ■

Optional

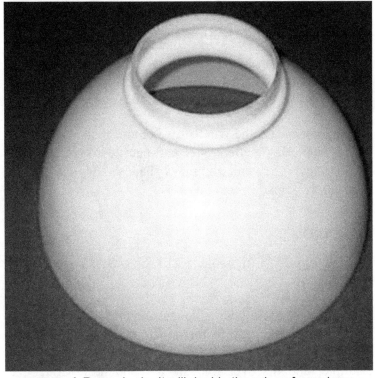

■ **ABOVE:** *A Rayo shade. It will double the price of your lamp.* ■

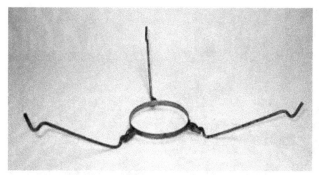

■ **ABOVE:** *A spider (shade-holder).* ■

You don't really need a shade for a Rayo to operate and throw off light. But the same is true of a conventional electric light bulb. Lots of light but rough on the eyes.

So-called gone-with-the-wind lamps (after the movie) were flat-wick kerosene lamps featuring two spherical globes. The bottom globe was the font, the part that held the kerosene. The top globe served as a shade. Shades of all styles came to be called globes, something of a misnomer. Geometrically, the Rayo shade is half a globe.

All this gone-with-the-wind stuff is more than you need to know but eBay sellers are jam-packed with incorrect terminology. They call chimneys shades. They call globes thingamabobbies.

Rayo wicks

You can buy NOS (new-old stock) Rayo wicks on eBay for about $6 each.

New-old stock? Sounds like an oxymoron. I was first introduced to the term in relation to antique automobiles. You might be restoring a 1929 Model 'A' Ford, for example, and discover for sale a brand new Model 'A' headlight, still sealed in the factory box. But the auto

44

supply store that originally sold that headlight went out of business decades ago. The headlight is brand new, never used. But it's also 90 years old and corroded. It is termed new-old stock.

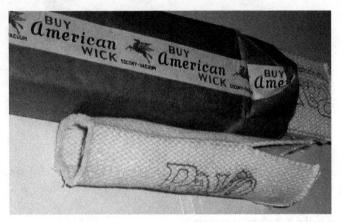

■ **ABOVE:** *Tubular Rayo wicks. NOS circa World War I, still in the wrapper. They work perfectly.* ■

Wicks don't last forever; they are gradually consumed in use. Thrifty housewives of years gone by did not throw out the old wick when it got short. Instead, they sewed the new wick to the old wick, nose to tail. I discovered just such a sewn-together wick on a Rayo that I disassembled after purchase. I had read about such an arrangement but had never actually seen it until then.

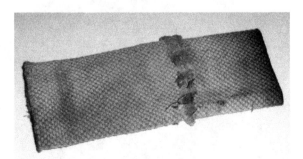

■ **ABOVE:** *Rayo wicks sewn nose-to-tail.* ■

45

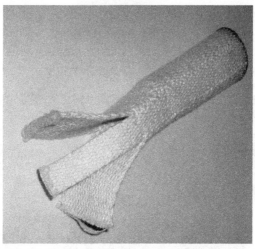

■ **ABOVE:** *You can make tubular center-draft wicks by sewing flat wicks into a tube. Use cotton thread; synthetics melt.)* ■

Changing a Rayo wick

Installing a new wick can be mystery to the first-time Rayo owner. With a conventional flat-wick lamp, a spur gear attached to a horizontal shaft digs into the cloth wick and forces it up and down as the wick-wheel on the shaft is turned. That's not how a Rayo operates.

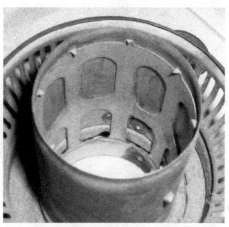

■ **ABOVE:** *Here we see the spurs that hold the wick in place.* ■

46

■ **ABOVE:** *To change the wick, first remove the flame spreader. It lifts off with a vertical pull.* ■

■ **ABOVE:** *Next, remove the gallery: lift-twist-lift it with the 'twist' being clockwise. Then unscrew the wick-riser assembly (counterclockwise). Here we see (L to R) the flame spreader, the gallery, the old wick still trapped inside the wick-riser assembly, and the font.* ■

47

With a Rayo, the tubular wick is trapped between two concentric metal tubes. The inner tube is rigid, fixed in place as part of the font. The outer tube is a carrier. The wick is held in the carrier by tiny spurs. When the wick-wheel is turned, the carrier travels up and down on a rack-and-pinion arrangement. The wick, in the grip of the spurs, travels up and down with the carrier. In a sense, the wick itself does not move at all; the carrier moves.

■ **ABOVE:** *Collapse the old wick and remove it.* ■

■ **ABOVE:** *Position the new wick in the carrier tube, flatten it against the walls of the tube, and press it onto the spurs. With*

the carrier in the full-down position, the wick must be slightly below the top of the carrier. ■

■ **ABOVE:** *Reassemble the lamp. The split in the bottom of the wick straddles the fixed inner tube. Tuck the tails into the font. Piece of cake, eh?* ■

Trimming a Rayo wick

The secret to obtaining maximum light from any wick-type lamp is to have the wick properly trimmed. With a tubular wick, the goal is to have a perfectly even height of flame all the way around the circle. If the flame is ½" high on the West side, it should be ½" high on the North, East, and South sides as well.

The 'proper' way to trim the wick is to first dip the top of the wick in kerosene (the wick having been installed in the carrier but not yet installed in the lamp), then install the carrier in the lamp and burn the wick dry. Scrape off the charred edge, using the wick tubes as a guide. The 'really proper' way is to scrape with your fingers, not a blade.

It's quicker to use a propane soldering torch. Raise the wick until a high side is exposed. Then char the high spot with your torch and scrape it off level. Keep repeating the process until the wick is dead-level all the way around. (And, no, it's not cheating.)

Chime dents

Rayo fonts were made in two halves, like two cereal bowls. The bowls were placed lip-to-lip. The joint was then folded over and soldered to prevent leaking. The seam is sometimes called a 'chime.'

A leaking chime can usually be resoldered and made leak-proof. You are probably better off not trying to straighten out any dent. Personally, I would hire a plumber to do the seam repair – someone with genuine expertise in soldering copper pipe joints. THINK SAFETY! Just like repairing an automobile gas tank, it is very important that the inside of the Rayo tank be empty and clean and dry before applying a torch to the outside.

■ **ABOVE LEFT:** *A simple dent. No problem.* **ABOVE RIGHT:** *A dented chime; a potential leaker.* ■

Stress cracks

All Rayos were made from nickel-plated brass. All. They're not chrome or silver. So-called *brass* Rayos are simply nickel-brass lamps that have had their nickel plating stripped off.

A certain percentage of lamps will exhibit stress cracking. Unfortunately, if you ask an eBay seller if his lamp is stress-cracked, he won't have any idea what you're talking about. Stress cracks are hairline cracks in the font through which kerosene can and will ooze. The cracks are caused by the way the lamp was made in the factory.

■ ABOVE: *You can see it with your eyes and feel it with your fingers but stress cracking is not obvious to the casual buyer.* ■

The two metal halves of a font were each manufactured by a process called spinning. The spinning process introduced 'work hardening' in the metal. If you bend a metal paper clip back-and-forth, back-and-forth, it will gradually become brittle and eventually snap. That's an example of work hardening.

Rayos were relatively cheap lamps so the very thinnest metal possible was used to spin the fonts. And it work hardened. The lamps looked fine when they left the factory. And they were fine – for twenty or thirty years. But tiny stress cracks from the work hardening finally began to appear. And kerosene will ooze through those cracks.

There are epoxy kits on the market used to coat and repair the inside of automobile gas tanks. The kits contain cleaning agents that you slosh around inside the tank followed by a liquid epoxy coating, also inside the tank.

I see no reason why the coatings wouldn't work on a stress-cracked Rayo although I, personally, have not tried it. Some of the brand names are Phenol Novolac, POR-15, Kreem, and Red-Kote. Their cost is in the $30-70 range.

Cracked galleries

The Rayo gallery (the part that holds the glass chimney) is a 'crown' style – so named because it resembles a king's crown. If you turn the gallery upside down, there is a metal sleeve attached to the crown. It is the sleeve's function to hold the gallery fast to the lamp. After many years of heating and cooling (i.e. expansion and contraction) the sleeve is sometimes cracked.

I have seen sleeves in everyday use that were cracked far worse than anything shown here. You can reinforce a cracked gallery with a stainless steel hose clamp. Enough clearance exists inside the lamp to reinstall the gallery with the clamp attached. The clamp becomes part of the lamp. You can't even see it afterwards.

■ **ABOVE:** *Gallery shown upside-down. This is a good one.* ■

■ **ABOVE:** *Badly cracked.* ■

■ **ABOVE:** *Cracked with hose clamp.* ■

Rayo competitors of yesteryear

The same lamp companies that made Rayos on contract for Standard Oil made their own centerdraft lamps. The big names of the day included The Rochester Lamp Co., Plume & Atwood, Edward Miller & Co. (made the Miller, the Juno, and several others), and B&H (Bradley and Hubbard).

The major difference between these manufacturers was in the system each one used to raise and lower the wick. Everybody did it differently. Nobody wanted to pay royalties on a competitor's patent. In that regard, Rayo was like the Volkswagen bug. It remained the same, decade after decade, with no model changes.

■ **ABOVE:** *A B&H Lamp (No. 4 Radiant). The fit and finish are much superior to a Rayo. Ditto the price. You're looking at a $300 lamp here.* ■

■ **ABOVE LEFT:** *This B&H lamp employs a Belgian #1 chimney, similar to the 'Matador' style. This hard-to-find chimney makes the No. 4 Radiant an orphan and therefore not a good choice for the survivalist.* **ABOVE RIGHT:** *The flame spreader pushes the flame out to fill the bulge. With a properly trimmed wick, you can get a tulip-shaped flame that climbs more than halfway up the bulge – much bigger than what's displayed here – midway between impressive and frightening.* ■

The antique centerdrafts were (and are) superb. You just can't find them. Or when you do, you can't afford them. Rayo is the exception. It's cheap, reliable, fixable.

KOSMOS & MATADOR

At first glance, the Kosmos looks like a small centerdraft. At the flame, the Kosmos wick forms a circle. The Kosmos wick, however, is not tubular or round. In lamper lingo, it's a 'flat-wick-formed-round.' You feed in a flat wick and the burner shapes it into a round tube.

■ **ABOVE:** *Note the alignment problem (here exaggerated for illustration purposes) at the seam as the wick is raised and forced into a tube. Rayo designers faced a somewhat similar problem, trying to keep all sides of the circle level as the wick was raised.* ■

■ **ABOVE:** *This is a 14''' Kosmos, the largest size commonly available. Spread flat, the wick is 2½" wide. The triple-apostrophe designation – ''' – stands for line or ligne. See the section above entitled 'Nominal Dimensions' for a discussion of ligne.* ■

The Kosmos was first produced in 1865 by Wild and Wessel, Germany. It was patented outside Germany but not in Germany itself. As a consequence, it was widely copied by competitors. Today the Kosmos is made by Gaudard in France. That means you can buy a new Kosmos; you needn't wait for an antique to show up on eBay. The bad news is that a Kosmos outputs only 25 watts-worth of light and costs around a hundred dollars.

■ **ABOVE LEFT:** *Kosmos chimneys are tall, skinny, and pricey –* *$15 plus postage on eBay.* **ABOVE RIGHT:** *By design, the flame is intended to run higher than the pinch in the chimney. But how high is too high?* <u>*Answer.*</u> *As long as it doesn't smoke, it is deemed okay.* ■

The Kosmos is a side-draft lamp, not centerdraft. Down inside the burner (where you can't see it) there is a big triangular gap that lets in air. The incoming air is directed to the center of the circular flame. But incoming air doesn't enter at the center, it comes in from the side. Aladdin-brand lamps (to be discussed in a future volume of The Non-Electric Lighting Series) are also side-draft lamps.

The Kosmos has a kissin' cousin named the Matador, introduced in 1895 by Ehrich and Graetz, Germany.

As just described, the *Kosmos* is a side-draft burner with a flat-wick-formed-round. Its **flame is elongated vertically** by a constriction in the chimney.

The *Matador* is a side-draft burner with a flat-wick-formed-round. Its **flame is expanded horizontally** by a flame spreader in a bulge-chimney (similar to the B&H shown earlier).

Like Kosmos, Matadors are still made today. Price-wise and candlepower-wise, they are pretty much on par with each other.

Although, mechanically, the Kosmos and Matador work great, from a light-generation, cost-effectiveness point of view there are many lamps that provide a bigger bang for the buck – the Rayo; portable propane lamps for camping; Coleman 200A and 220 (there are hundreds on eBay at any given moment); Coleman 214 and 285 (available new); and Mr Heater (wall-mounted natural gas or propane lamps). These all produce more candlepower for less money.

But because the Kosmos is sold today on the Internet – hyped might be a better word – it's something you need to understand.

AFTERWORD

This concludes our discussion of wick-fed kerosene lamps. The topic of kerosene *pressure* lanterns will have its own book in the not-too-distant future.

So far, on the general theme of *lighting*, I've published several books, articles, and YouTube videos. This seems as good a place as any to itemize them.

- ***Book 1: Candles*** (from The Non-Electric Lighting Series). Available from Amazon as both a Kindle ebook and as a paperback.

- ***Book 2: Olive Oil Lamps &c.*** (from The Non-Electric Lighting Series). Available from Amazon as both a Kindle ebook and as a paperback.

- ***Book 3: Lamp Fuels*** (from The Non-Electric Lighting Series). Available from Amazon as both a Kindle ebook and as a paperback.

- ***The NEW 2000-Hour Flashlight.*** Available from Amazon as both a Kindle ebook and as a paperback.

- ***Lanterns, Lamps & Candles: A User's Guide.*** On CD. Available from www.rc-publishing.com; 442 color photos; 70,000 words.

- ***Propane for Preppers.*** A 5-part series on Gaye Levy's blog, *Backdoor Survival* (free)

- ***Converting a Gas Lantern to Kerosene.*** A YouTube how-to video, 11 minutes long (free).